VELJO TORMIS

PIISPA
JA
PAKANA

THE BISHOP AND THE PAGAN

FOR MALE CHORUS AND SOLOISTS

 FENNICA GEHRMAN

Veljo Tormis
PIISPA JA PAKANA
The Bishop and the Pagan
(1992/1995)
for male chorus and soloists

The story of The Bishop and the Pagan, drawn from musical documents and folklore, tells of the death of the British warrior and Christian missionary Bishop Henry at the hands of the Finnish peasant farmer Lalli near the town of Turku (Åbo) in the winter of 1158. By a fortunate and unusual historical circumstance, the viewpoints of both sides have been preserved: a written Latin Gregorian chant "The Sequence of Saint Henry" documents the British Christian side, and numerous folk songs represent the event as seen by the Finnish pagan.

Piispa ja pakana

Piiskop ja pagan

The Bishop and the Pagan

Text: a) The Sequence of St. Henry, transcribed by Tuomo Pekkanen
b) Ancient Finnish runic folk songs, adapted by Sakari Puurunen

Veljo Tormis
1992/1995

---

*) The cast of soloists may be changed (e.g. Altos 1,2 + Tenor or Alto + Tenors 1,2). The parts may be doubled or interchanged during the perfomance.

**) ⌐ - rest of variable length

***) ◻ - note of variable length

****) pronounced: homm

The original ensemble version was commissioned for The King's Singers by the 14th Musik-Biennale Berlin 1993

④

praesulis celebritas.

I

II hum

p

hum hum hum hum

⑤ II mf molto legato quasi gregoriana ⑥

Quem e - le - git, quem di - le - xit, quem or - na - vit,

mf

(p)

hum hum

⑦

quem pro - ve - xit, in sub - li - me quem e - re - xit

hum hum hum hum

↘ - basic melody

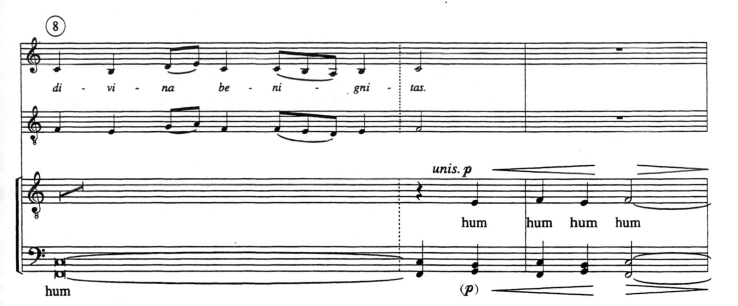

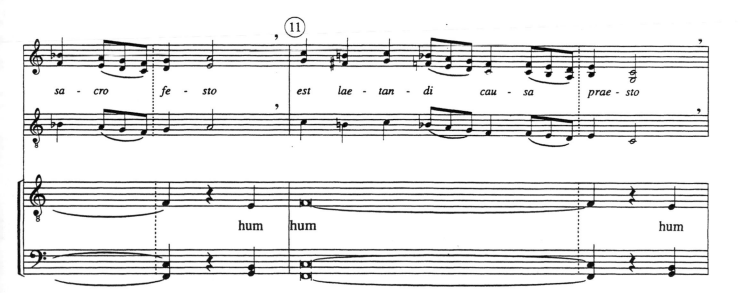

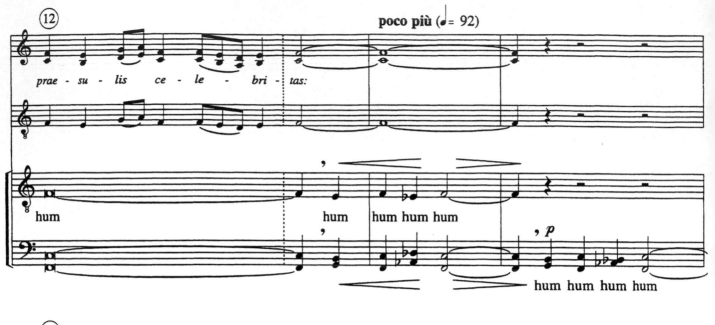

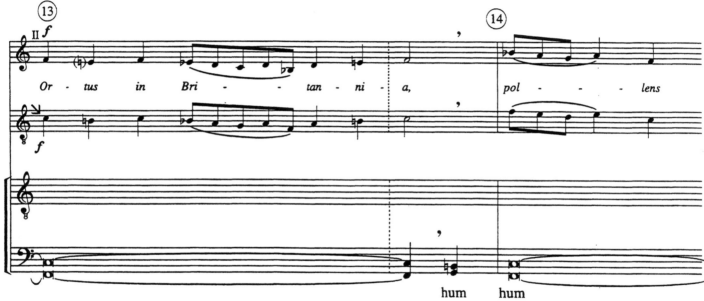

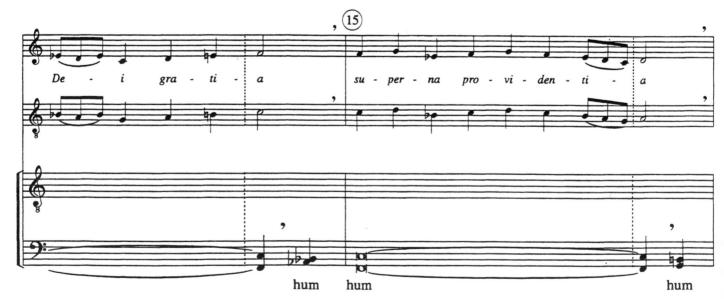

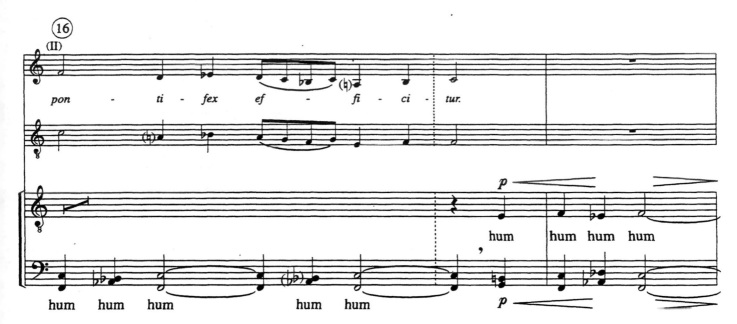

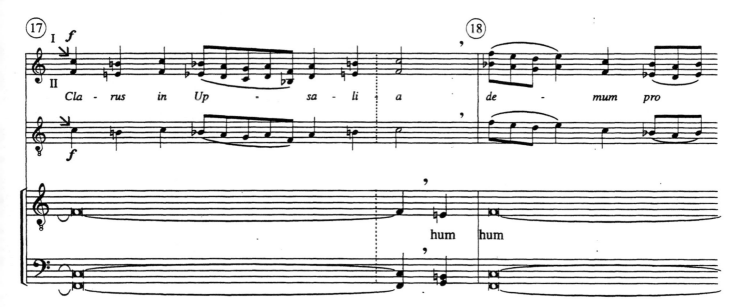

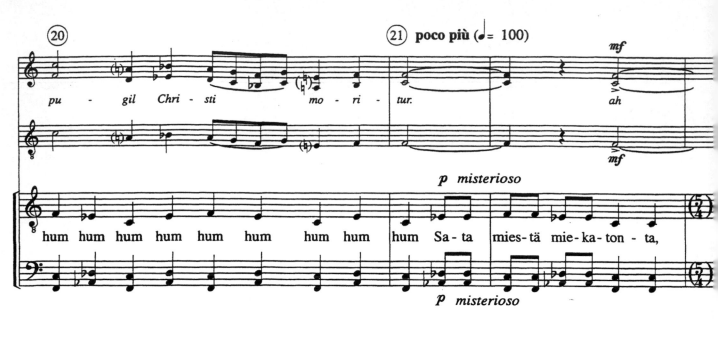

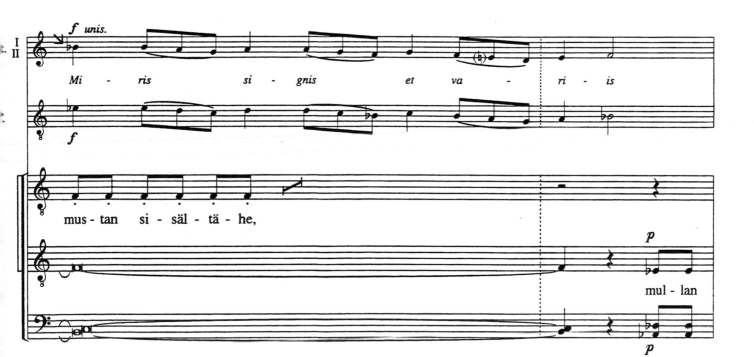

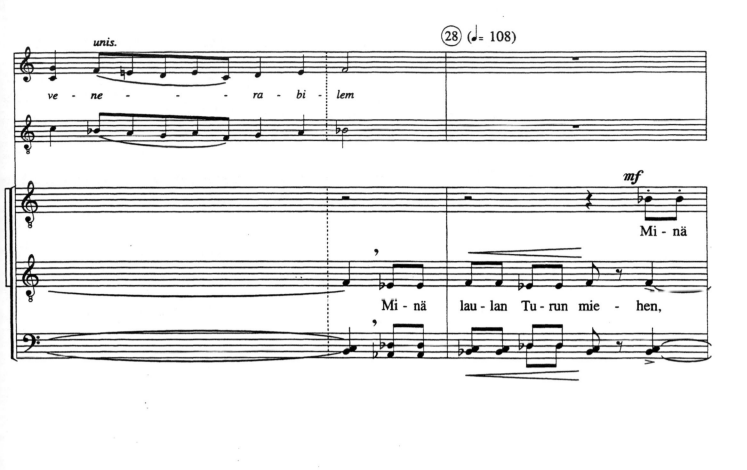

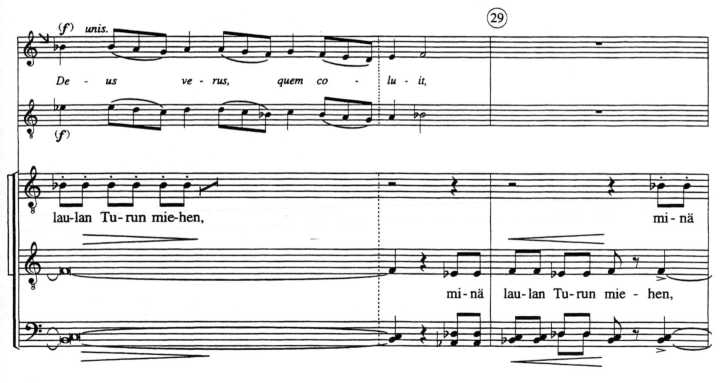

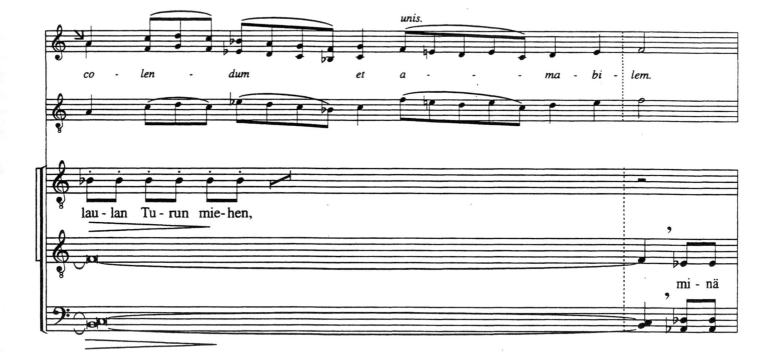

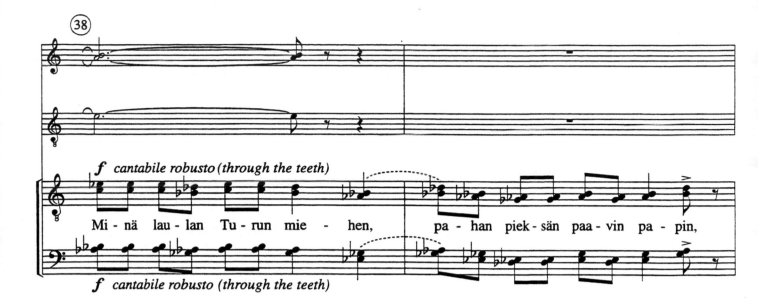

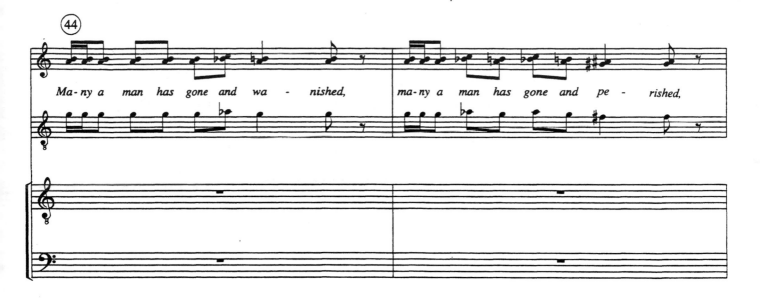

Ma- ny a man has gone and wa - nished, ma- ny a man has gone and pe - rished,

few have safe - ly come a - gain.

mi - nä, mi - nä lau - lan Tu - run mie - hen,

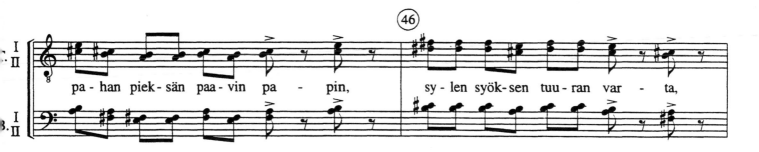

pa - han piek- sän paa - vin pa - pin, sy - len syök - sen tuu - ran var - ta,

kir - ve- hel - la kut- kut - te - len! Mi - nä, mi - nä,

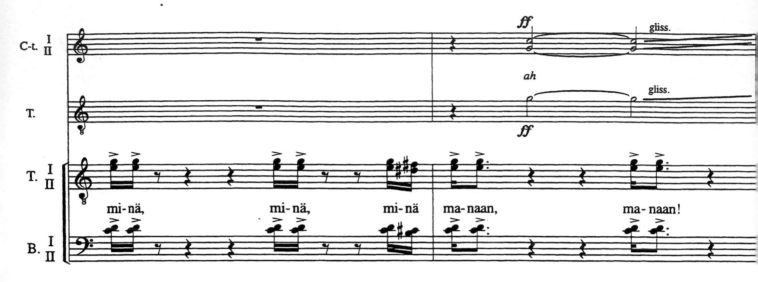

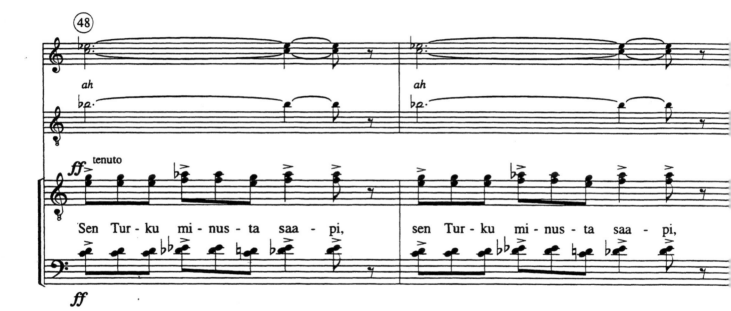

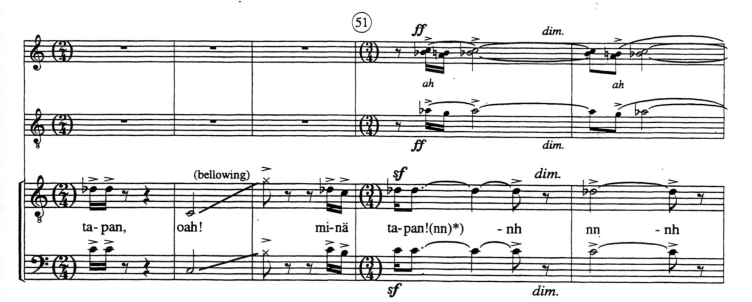

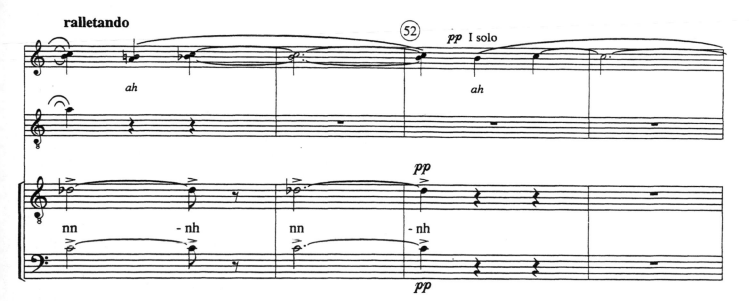

*) nasal sound

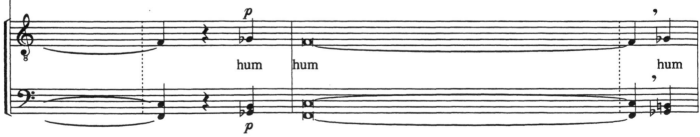

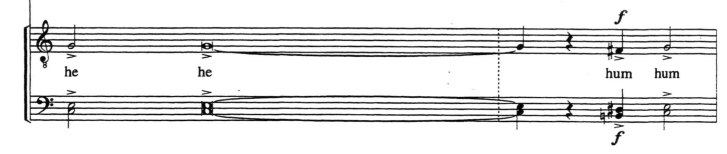

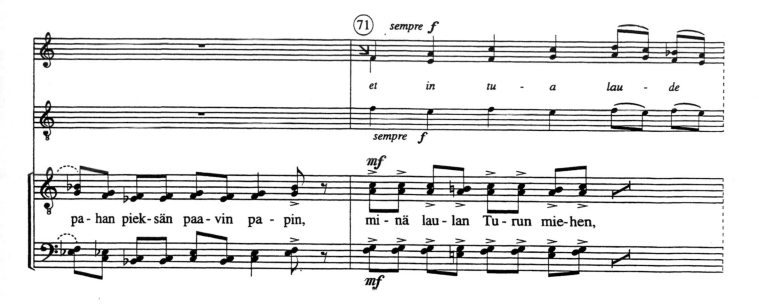

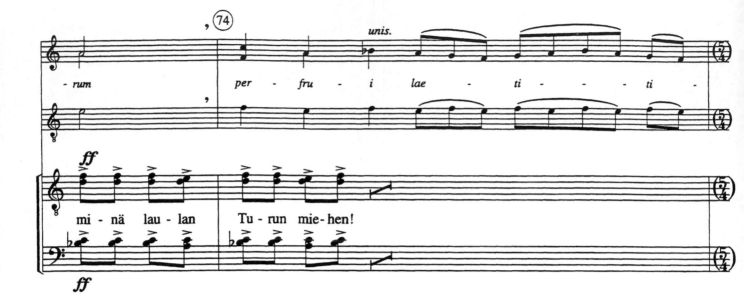

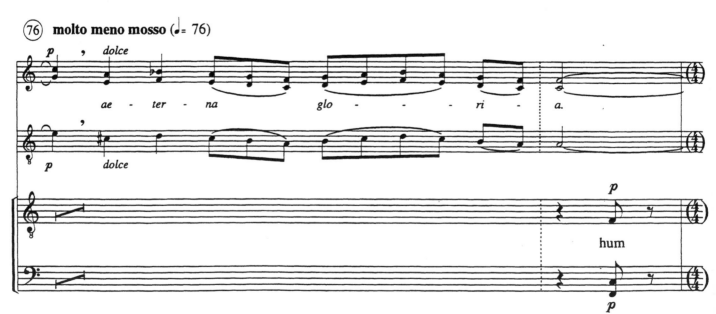

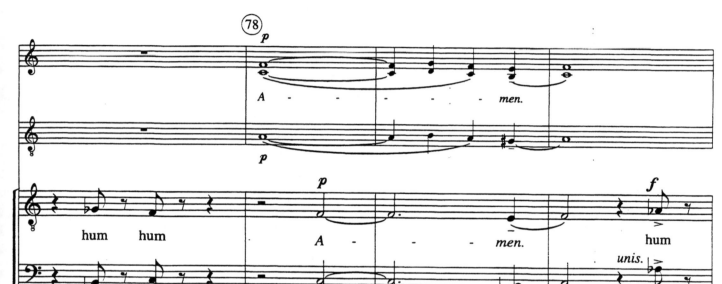

Piispa ja pakana
I. De santo Henrico sequentia

Coetus noster laetus esto
pro Henrici sacro festo
est laetandi causa praesto
    praesulis celebritas.

Quem elegit, quem dilexit,
quem ornavit, quem provexit,
in sublime quem erexit
    divina benignitas.

Ortus in Britannia,
pollens Dei gratia,
superna providentia
    pontifex efficitur.

Clarus in Upsalia,
demum pro iustitia
decertans in Finlandia
    pugil Christi moritur.

Miris signis et variis
sanctum suum prodigiis
declarat venerabilem
Deus verus, quem coluit,
amavit atque docuit
    colendum et amabilem.

Martyr Dei, iam laborum
et mercede tormentorum
summo bono sine metu
et Sanctorum fruens coetu
    in aeterna gloria.

Te laudantem nostrum coetum
et in tua laude laetum
fac in coetu Angelorum
sempiterna beatorum
    perfrui laetitia.
Amen.

Transcribed by Tuomo Pekkanen

II. Ancient Finnish *runo* songs

Sata miestä miekatonta,
tuhat miestä miekallista,
kaikki miehet vaaran alta,
mullan mustan sisältähe.

Minä laulan Turun miehen,
pahan pieksän paavin papin,
sylen syöksen tuuran vartta,
kirvehellä kutkuttelen!

Minun veljeni Henrikki,
älä mene maalle Suomen!
Kyll' on sinne monta mennyt,
mutt' ei ole jälleen tullut
eikä paljo palannut.

Minä, minä, minä
manaan, minä manaan!
Sen Turku minusta saapi,
pajattaapi paavin pappi,
kiittelevi Ristin Kiesus.
Sen Turku saapi!

Tapan, tapan, minä tapan!

· Finnish texts adpted by Sakari Puurunen
Translated by Kaja Koppel

The Bishop and the Pagan
I. The Sequence of Saint Henry

Our happy brotherhood
on the holy feast of Henry
is gathered to rejoice
    in the fame of this saint.

Who was chosen, who was loved,
who was adorned, who was elevated,
who was lifted up on high ·
    by divine generosity.

Born in Britain,
strong by the grace of God,
by supernal providence
    made a priest,

Bishop in Upsala,
then fighting
for justice in Finland,
    he died a gladiator for Christ.

By wondrous and manifold signs
and portents
he proclamed praiseworthy
the true God who had fostered him,
loved and taught him,
    caring and kind.

God's martyr, now in recompense
for your labors and torments
enjoying without fear the blessings
and the company of the saints
    in eternal glory,

To our brotherhood, praising you
and rejoicing in your praise,
grant that we, in the company
of the ever-blesssed angels,
    may partake of joy.
Amen.

II. Calling Dead Forefathers for Help

A hundred swordless men,
a thousand sworded men,
all the men from under a hill,
from the black earth.

It is I who casts a spell over the man from Turku,
 thrashes the Pope's bad priest,
spits him with the ice pick,
tickles him with the axe.

My brother, dearest Henry,
do not depart for Finland!
many a man has gone and vanished,
many a man has gone and perished,
few have safely come again.

It is I, I, I
who is cursing him, cursing him!
That is what Turku gets from me,
and the Pope's garrulous priest,
and the hymning Cross-bringer.
That is what Turku gets!

I'll kill him, kill him kill him!